CU00660662

# They Don't Award Nobel Prizes to Dead People

Sustainable service and work in our performance and
achievement orientated world

**Richard Nellis van Zyl-Smit**

They Don't Award Nobel Prizes to Dead People
Richard Nellis van Zyl-Smit

Printed in South Africa

ISBN: 978-0-6208088-5-9

Illustrations Zach Stewart

For those who dare greatly but accept they are flawed

# 1. Foreword

I had asked Professor Bongani Mayosi to write the foreword for this book, but he died tragically before completing it.

In honour of the amazing person he was – I have left the foreword blank

## 2. Introduction

On a typical dark and stormy winter's evening in Cape Town recently, whilst driving home up Ou Kaapse Weg pass, several cars were flashing their lights at me. I could not work out what they were trying to warn me of. I had my lights on. I was not driving excessively fast. It was not until I had crested the mountain pass that I came across the reason – a broken down car with no headlights on, stranded in the middle of the road. I was very grateful for the warning once I realised why I was being warned. The Porsche driver behind me, however was not interested: He quickly speeded past and overtook me after we had passed the stranded car, clearly frustrated at my uncertainty as to the meaning of the warning lights!

Arriving at my mid-career point in my own personal, intense and dark rain storm, has provided an opportunity to reflect. A number of issues relating to work and life have arisen; especially the legacy I might want to leave and how to ensure that I do more than 'survive my life'. And so, this short book was born out of a period of personal storms, where the edge was far too close for comfort and where the daily drive to work felt like I had swallowed a brick. To contemplate anything beyond the day ahead of me caused far too much anxiety.

That storm has passed. It has taken longer than I would have liked, but I hope that by sharing some of my reflections and experiences, I might help prevent some readers from going through those same storms. For those already in a storm of their own, may this book provide a hope for the light that you are not yet able to see.

The title of this book is derived from a real-life event that occurred in 2011. I was in New York at the time working as a post-doctoral fellow. The Nobel Prize for medicine was jointly awarded to Ralf Steinman who had discovered "dendritic cells" (the specialized cells that marshal your innate immune system and have been key to understanding how our body defends against infection) and two other researchers; Bruce Beutler and Jules Hoffman, who also had done work on the immune system.

Steinman actually discovered dendritic cells back in 1973 as a young research fellow. On 30 September 2011, he dies after battling pancreatic cancer for some time. The Nobel prize winners were announced three days later, and the award was shared between the three researchers. The problem was that Steinman was dead, and Nobel prizes are never awarded posthumously. The Nobel committee were not aware he had just died. Much speculation ensued as to what would happen to his award and whether or not they should now withdraw the award as he was no longer alive. They eventually decided to award him the prize and his family received it on his behalf. This is, to the best of my knowledge the only time that a Nobel prize has been awarded posthumously.

The parallels in this story fall flat quite quickly if you wish to be picky or pedantic: Firstly, his discovery was actually made 38 years prior to his death and secondly, he did receive the award even though he had died, so it was not the work that killed him.

I qualified as a doctor over 20 years ago and have worked with many people who have shaped my career, and my thinking about what is important in life. This book is not intended to be a critique on academia or clinical medicine, nor a "5 steps to improving your mental health and medical career". It was born out of a very difficult time which I had not anticipated. It required me to acknowledge my shortcomings, to reflect on how I had got into the present situation and how I was going to get out of it.

I am pretty certain that I am not on course for a Nobel prize and that most who read this book won't be either. But bear with me as I walk you through some reflections on why being alive just in case you receive a Nobel prize remains a good idea.

## 3. Being Trained to Cope

From an early age we are taught and encouraged to cope. Be it with homework, sport or music lessons; the better you can cope with failure or success, the further along the path you can go. We must learn to cope. For some, coping may not be taught or encouraged early on, but may develop as a requirement of where we find ourselves in life and work. We are all in this world together; those that are healthy, those that can cope, those that are not so adept at coping and those that have illnesses.

Those of us who are able, trained and capable need to support those that are unable, untrained and incompetent. Generally, that is how our social systems are constructed. The extent to which we support is a topic for someone else's book. But I think overall, few of us match up to Nelson Mandela or Mother Theresa, or even Albert Einstein or Bill Gates. Our sphere of influence and impact is likely to be much smaller. However, in academia and research our impact often extends well beyond ourselves as our world includes many colleagues, students, research papers and patients across the globe.

The question of how much we sacrifice of ourselves, our family and our health, to accomplish what we ultimately achieve in life, needs to be a personal decision. It will be shaped by a whole mix of intrinsic desires, personal circumstances, and external forces. That being said, in the high pressured, achievement orientated world we find ourselves in, not being able to cope is seen as a failure, which brings a whole new set of problems that we will discuss later.

"If you can't handle the heat – get out of the kitchen".

Especially in medicine, we have to cope. Our patients rely on us, they depend on us and we have to keep up with the latest research publications, and we have to …. The option of not coping, is never entertained. Our on-call rotations don't allow for it. Our hospital systems and services don't allow for it. Certainly, our colleagues are not that excited if you are taking a day off because you are not coping, as they have to pick up the slack and fill in for you when you are not around.

The fact that we are copers and have been trained to do so, enables us to go far beyond our limits, to where we should not be. We cope with far more than what we realistically can manage, and so when the metaphorical dam wall starts to show signs of cracking, the consequences are significantly more dreadful. Where others might have only been able to build a small barrier using a few twigs to hold back a little stream, we are so skilled at coping that we have built huge dam walls, holding back flood water. The implications of our dam wall cracking are far worse than a stream flowing over a barrier of twigs; family, personal and work life suffer far more.

This idea became real when I had to confront the fact that I was not coping. Everything I had been trained to do: to manage, to excel, to lead teams, to pursue excellence, not to make mistakes, not to not fail; it was all up for grabs. I had missed the metaphorical warning lights in the storm. The warning signs were clearly visible and flashing brightly. Thankfully they were noticed, not by me, but by someone who was on the lookout. I am grateful to those eyes that took the time to notice the warning lights and not let me ignore them.

To own up to this fact, acknowledge it and then very reluctantly to accept the necessary help, kept me from the edge and frankly it kept me from burn out. I had never thought I was even close to burn out, and so was not looking for the signs, but others did on my behalf. I know of some who have seen and ignored the warning lights, who had not acknowledged their situation and have suffered because of this.

So if you are a high achiever, competent and have a position with much responsibility but are failing to cope, can't cope, and have not been coping for some time; how do you read the warning lights?

It was a wise senior colleague who took some time out with me to explain the reality of where I was. It was precisely because I could cope so well that I had got into the situation that I found myself in. If I was not so adept at coping, I would have already cracked a long time ago. It was a very hard pill to swallow; to accept that I was broken, that despite multiple academic papers, qualifications and research accomplishments, I was flawed.

No reflections on Leonard Cohen's "cracked bells... that's how the light gets in", or comments like "it makes us human", "you will be stronger for it" provided any semblance of reassurance or lessened the blow to my self-esteem and my academic ego. I was not at all ready to wear the label of failed or couldn't cope, and so I very reluctantly accepted help. I started taking medication to help me to get through each day, to lessen the relentless ache in my stomach, and panic attacks that would hit at 3 a.m. I am very grateful that I no longer see 3 a.m. unless on-call and have found some normality to my sleep patterns. I continue to work out what it means to be a cracked bell in an academic world of performance and perfection, where only excellence is praised, where the best is all that is celebrated, and failure is just that: failure.

Don't think for a moment that I am not one hundred percent committed to academic excellence, or that I wouldn't celebrate other peoples' success. I would be quite happy to be publishing in the 'big journals' or being featured as an up and coming researcher. I am neither supporting nor advocating the notion of substandard or 'just par' work ethics. It is just that in many environments, especially that of academia, if you are not playing with the 'big boys and girls' (and winning) you are somehow made to feel like a failure.

The ability to endure criticism, and to get back up multiple times after facing rejection from funding bodies or prestigious journals, is what it takes to make it at the top. I admire some people's ability to stay the course and allow the regular rejection of what they are offering to flow over them with little apparent consequence. They have been trained to cope and cope they do. But sometimes I just wonder: at what cost and is it worth it?

A great deal of introspection and reflection is required to understand what we do, its importance and how we cope with it. In clinical medicine particularly, we make life and death decisions, and then "go home for dinner". We make decisions affecting people's lives, their careers and their livelihood. The pressures are relentless with a never-ending stream of sick patients needing assistance.

The research world is slightly different with less of those life and death decisions, but with a continual need to find funding and to convince the people who hold the purse strings that what you are wanting to do is important. Added to this is the pressure to publish and the need to convince a journal editorial board it is worth publishing. Then you start again, and the cycle repeats itself over and over again.

Coping is part and parcel of the terrain, the better you can cope with failure and rejection, the longer you can survive. But surely survival is not a long-term goal? Are we all just aiming to cope? Not coping then becomes a potentially fatal option.

Coping is not the goal. We need to seek an alternative approach to our lives and careers that does not have survival as the primary outcome and coping as the mechanism to get there.

# 4. Don't Leave it all on the Field

Some years back, I attended a conference and heard a very engaging American speaker called Albert Tate. He was speaking at the Global Leadership Summit and his message was essentially: "don't leave it all on the field". What a crazy idea in a leadership meeting! We were expecting to hear about how to give our all and to go the extra mile. A talk about putting our whole heart and soul into what we do, so that we can succeed. His entire message was at odds with the sporting concept of 'leaving it all out on the field'. This is the notion that every time we 'go out there', be it at work, a presentation or a meeting, we should give everything we have and come back with 'nothing'. The idea is to empty your tank on the field so that you are certain you gave your all to the cause at hand.

The problem with 'leaving it all out on the field' as he enthusiastically pointed out, is that you have nothing left when you get home. Having nothing left for those not on the field, may be good for those on the field, but not those off it. This saying brings out a tension between doing your best "leaving it all out on the field" and saving some of yourself "slacking off". Now clearly these are not the appropriate converses – but this is often what we pick up: if we could have done better, if we could have done more, if we could just have … the outcome might have been different.

It is hard to judge this from a personal perspective as we are often only able to see it from our own viewpoint. Until someone else looks at the situation with a greater perspective, we continue to berate ourselves for not doing enough. The other challenge is to know if you could have done the same, achieved as much, without sacrificing your relationships, family and personal health.

In the medical field this is tangibly evident when we have a patient dying in front of us. A junior doctor often needs a senior colleague to say: "Stop, you can't do anymore," or, "Nothing you can do is going to change the outcome for this patient." This may seem extreme, but it is part of growing up as a doctor and understanding when more time on the field won't make a difference. It is not about conceding the game or throwing in the towel, it is recognizing and acknowledging that we need to stop so that we can fight again another day.

This is less tangible in research and academia, when promotion, funding and success are often viewed as proportional to the effort we put in. The numbers of hours worked in the lab, the time taken to prepare the grant application, the numerous iterations of a manuscript prior to submission. To judge when something is good enough is difficult. This is confounded by the outcomes: often what we offer is good, even excellent, but for some extraneous reason our grant is rejected, our manuscript turned down or the experiment fails. The thought, 'I should have done more' begins. This then drives our guilt and we choose to work harder. The fear of failure is realised if we don't succeed. Performance anxiety can be crippling when we fear even trying. In the following chapter I will expand on this idea of the voices we listen to with reference to a quote from a man named Anton Ego.

As an intern (junior doctor) working on the general medical ward at Groote Schuur Hospital, wanting to be conscientious and to make sure that I provided the best for all my patients, I got into a habit of "fixing up the blue boards". A blue board is the prescription chart on which doctors write the medication for a specific patient. Apparently it used to be blue, but in our day it had become black and white, however retaining the name blue board. This critical piece of paper contained the instructions to the nursing staff about monitoring vital signs. It gave the prescribed medication dose and timing, and any other special instructions such as whether the patient could eat or not. With rushed and half-asleep doctors, the board frequently became a mess, and I would spend time making sure the writing was legible, that everything was neat and if need be, re-written.

One day my registrar (senior doctor) on call admonished me and instructed me to stop doing that and go home, not because the blue boards were neat enough, but that making them any neater would not materially change the level of care or outcomes of the patients. The lesson I learnt that day and remember over 20 years later, was that at some point, any more time that you spend does not improve or alter the outcome. The time I spent in the hospital doing that was burning energy and ability that should be saved for other activities at home, doing something that had an outcome with a far more important impact.

We are not taught to tailor our efforts, we are not encouraged to 'just pass'; we are implored to do our best, to give everything we have to the cause. As a patient this is the kind of doctor you want, right? You want the doctor who has done their level best, the doctor who has given everything to you. But what about them, what have they given to themselves? What about us? Is there a middle ground where we can give our best, but leave something for when we are not on the field?

Why does the medical profession have such a high rate of suicide and drug abuse? In the USA a recent publication estimated that 14% of male and 26% of female surgeons were abusing alcohol (Oreskovich 2012). I would suggest the reason for this is that we leave too much on the field and have nothing left for ourselves, our marriages or our children.

We need to know our boundaries; we need to know where our limits are and work within them. World class athletes only push themselves to the limits on a few occasions. In the final of a major competition such as the world championships or the Olympics, an enormous amount is at stake and they will give their all. But be assured in the preliminary rounds and on every other occasion, they are providing a high performance, but it is measured effort. Leaving it all on the field every day is not a sustainable option.

## 5. Man in the Arena

One of my favourite authors is Brené Brown, a social work professor in Houston Texas. She has written some amazing books on facing your fears and daring greatly. (Brown 2012) Essentially her premise is to show up, be brave and dare greatly. Knowing who you are and why you are doing what you are doing is not something that we get taught at school or university, certainly not in medical school when I trained. We tend to stumble upon our motivations as we go along, or we are forced to choose when options present themselves rather than taking the time early on in our lives to clearly define who we are and what we are wanting out of life and our job.

In medicine particularly, we can progress pretty far into our career before we need to make a major decision as to where we are wanting to go or how to get there. The sense of calling, to help save lives is strong in some. In others the academic prowess and publication record is the motivating factor. In others it is simply the drive to make a whole lot of money. The internal motivation can be influenced heavily by our experiences, peers and senior mentors, so that what started out in one direction may change radically for good or bad. The voices that we choose to listen to, influence and shape us more than I think we sometimes care to acknowledge.

The pressures to deliver, especially in academic medicine are inherent in the job, as the saying goes: 'Publish or perish.' This is a subject for other books, so I will not digress into the merits of the system. I will however say that too much pressure to publish has the undesired consequence of producing rubbish or even fraudulent scientific outputs. In medicine, as in many other occupations, there are one too many stories of young and promising individuals making errors of judgment and going down irrecoverable paths to destruction. My impression is that much of this is a function of the voices that are listened to and what is being modelled by one's peers and senior colleagues.

Decision fatigue, from unrelenting pressure or stress, often leads to poor judgment in an acutely stressful situation. These poor decisions might be mitigated against by the people 'in your corner' filtering and reflecting on these voices with and for you. Making firm decisions as to how you will respond in certain situations can also help mitigate poor decision making. More about this later.

In Brené Brown's book *Daring Greatly* she quotes an excerpt from a speech made by Theodore Roosevelt in Paris on 23 April 1910 entitled the 'Citizenship in a Republic'. The entire speech is 18 pages long but within this speech is the excerpt referred to as the 'Man in the arena':

*"It is not the critic who counts; not the man who points out how the strong man stumbles, or where the doer of deeds could have done them better. The credit belongs to the man who is actually in the arena, whose face is marred by dust and sweat and blood; who strives valiantly; who errs, who comes short again and again, because there is no effort without error and shortcoming; but who does actually strive to do the deeds; who knows great enthusiasms, the great devotions; who spends himself in a worthy cause; who at the best knows in the end the triumph of high achievement, and who at the worst, if he fails, at least fails while daring greatly, so that his place shall never be with those cold and timid souls who neither know victory nor defeat." (Roosevelt 1910)*

This quote is in part, the inspiration for the title of Brown's book *Daring Greatly*. The message is show up in the arena, and give your all, and if you fail, do so valiantly. In addition, the first line of the quote refers to the critic. Brown draws the parallels of how those passing comment from the 'cheap seats' in the arena affect us. She made the decision that she would not listen to the voices from people sitting in the audience, but only those who were actually in the arena, those "marred with the same blood and dirt". The rest were simply providing comment that was neither valid nor worth listening to.

She recounts having presented a TED talk on the topic of shame and vulnerability, her research focus as a social work professor. In the following days, against advice from close friends, she read comments online from people who had watched the TED talk. Some criticised her dress sense, her weight and others pitied her family. She recalls in a bemusing way, eating a tub of ice cream in an attempt to dull the critique. It makes the sober point of identifying whose criticism we choose to listen to, and whose criticism would be better to avoid. More importantly, whose criticism should we allow ourselves to be influenced by and internalise?

In reading her book, and listening to her TED talks, I realized that the voices around me were not only influencing how I approached things, but also how I felt about my achievements or lack of them. I was listening to comments from those who appeared to be in the academic medicine and research arena. I assumed they were covered in the same dust and blood, but actually may not have been as marred as it appeared. The decisions I had made, placed me in a different situation where I was functioning in more than one arena, and there were less voices truly covered in the same blood and dust.

How does one balance receiving valid feedback and receiving criticism from those 'in the know'? How do we orientate ourselves when receiving feedback? Do we lean in to hear the heart of the feedback, or do we hold back and let most of the feedback fall at our feet? This in turn influences how we position ourselves and treat others when we ourselves are the ones providing feedback. Each of us has our own story, our own history, present circumstance and perceived or hoped for future. Few will fully understand where we are currently and our capacity to engage and endure unless they are walking very closely with us. Before we make judgements about ourselves we need to ensure that it is based on feedback from those that are indeed covered in the same dust and mud that covers us.

What we have proposed, be it work, grants or publications, may not be up to someone else's standards or expectations, but this should not impact on our own sense of self-worth or how we see ourselves. That should be reserved for those people in our corner, which we will come to later. It is however not always easy to separate what we offer from who we are, and how we feel about ourselves. This is especially true if everyone else around us seems to be successfully pursuing the same rewards with either minimal or potentially insignificant sacrifice.

This brings me to one of my favourite quotes which was printed out and stuck on the wall in our research fellows' office early in my PhD training days. At the time feedback was aplenty and came from many sources. Understanding whose voice I was listening to, and what I was internalising regarding who I was and not what I did, became vitally important. The quote comes from a man called Anton Ego, not a name many would know; he is a central character in an animated movie of all places!

Ratatouille was a Pixar movie released in 2007, the year I started my PhD. I can highly recommend the movie. Its central character is a rat called Remy, who wanted to be a cook. After leaving his house in the country, he arrives in Paris and through a series of adventures, eventually makes it and cooks at a famous restaurant in Paris called Gusteau's. The food critic Anton Ego is not a fan of Gusteau's and had previously slated the food at the restaurant. One evening Ego arrives to make his final pronouncement on the new chef and food at Gusteau's. Remy is in fact the one cooking in the kitchen and makes a traditional and simple ratatouille. On eating the ratatouille, Ego is instantly transported back to his childhood and his mother's cooking. Without spoiling the movie for anyone who still wishes to see it Ego has an epiphany and writes a review on the restaurant food which appears in the next morning's newspaper.

It is not so much about the food (which was made by a rat and was spectacular), but about the critic and the criticism that he focusses on:

*"In many ways, the work of a critic is easy. We risk very little yet enjoy a position over those who offer up their work and their selves to our judgment. We thrive on negative criticism, which is fun to write and to read. But the bitter truth we critics must face is that, in the grand scheme of things, the average piece of junk is probably more meaningful than our criticism designating it so."* (Ratatouille 2007)

This quote has oddly become a central part of my filter to feedback. Not that I am, nor that what I offered is in fact junk, just that others perceive it to be so.

We need to be careful not to become immune or unresponsive to legitimate and valid feedback, but to recognise when it is indeed just negative criticism. Even when it is dressed up as constructive feedback, it has no bearing on why we did what we did in the first place and does not change who we are. What it is, is just that: feedback, which may or may not be of value.

Over a recent breakfast meeting with some good friends, I was recounting Ego's story and that I was writing this book. One of them commended me for writing it, to which I instantly responded, "But you have not read it yet." He retorted almost immediately that it was not what he thought about the book that mattered, it was just that it was being written!

The challenge to all of us whose work must be reviewed: Consider how much additional work, adaptation or re-evaluation is required, or whether we need merely to note and file the feedback without taking it on board. In addition, we should not internalise it, or allow it to influence who we are in the greater scheme of things. Passing this lesson on to our trainees, our junior staff or colleagues, removes some of the angst included in submitting written work or giving a presentation. We should strive to separate our feedback about the person from the work ('junk') that has been offered up, and in turn encourage the recipient of the feedback to do the same.

It requires some effort to sift through the feedback, to find the nuggets of gold hidden within the junk. There may be some truth hidden in the rubble disguised as feedback. It may be truth, even if expressed unkindly, it remains truth. The challenge when receiving feedback is not to dismiss it all as criticism, without looking for the truth, and equally not to throw ourselves onto the metaphorical pile of rubble as well.

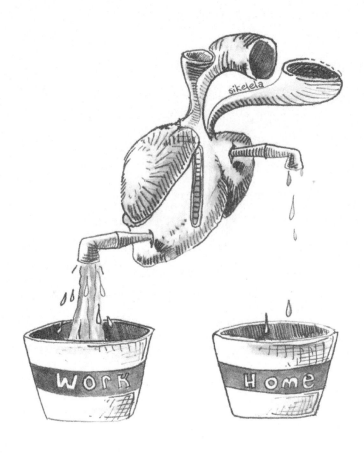

# 6. Sacrifice

"A sacrifice is not a sacrifice unless it is a sacrifice." I am not sure who this quote is originally attributed to, but it has a measure of truth worth exploring. There are many problems that arise around the concept of sacrifice: not only for the person who is doing the sacrificing, but sometimes for the object, activity or person being sacrificed.

There is an urban legend in our medical community about a story of a young researcher who was planning on taking his soon to be fiancé out for dinner in the evening. He receives a call from his Professor who wants him to finish working on a manuscript that evening so that it can be submitted to the Lancet (one of the top three most prestigious medical journals). When protesting that he had important dinner plans, the Professor responded: "My boy, orgasms come and go – but a Lancet paper is forever".

One major problem with a sacrifice is that we don't always know at the outset how much we need to sacrifice for the particular cause. It is only after the outcome has been achieved, that we can reflect on what it cost to get to that point. The nagging question is: Could we have sacrificed less to get to the same outcome? If something is worth doing, it is clearly worth doing properly, but how do we judge what properly means? People judge our efforts before the outcome is known, and then deride our lack of willingness to sacrifice for the cause if the outcome is not the desired one. It is not only our sacrifice and what we lose, but the sacrifice of those around us, who lose us. It may result in becoming an absent parent, or even just a parent who is too busy to play. Our children and friends may lose out on time spent with us, which might seem trivial to us, but may have a bigger impact on them.

The scientist who discovers the cure for AIDS will be lauded for his or her efforts and almost unlimited sacrifices would be commended and considered worthy in the name of the greater cause. A cure for AIDS would impact so many people and change the world, that most would accept the cost of a broken marriage or a dysfunctional relationship with their children and maybe even prescription drug dependence? But what about a lesser discovery of a new treatment for AIDS, or a new test for AIDS? For each of these outcomes we have a personal estimation of how much we would be prepared to sacrifice. I hasten to add that these will be very different from person to person and especially from a director compared to a junior researcher or clinician.

When I was at University, I was a serious runner and competed one year at the Foot of Africa Marathon. A small group of runners had formed up front including a former winner of one of South Africa's most prestigious ultra-marathons. The conversation in our group was around finding the time to train and many were lamenting the fact that they could not find enough time to train with all of their life and work commitments. This particular runner then chirped in and effectively shut down the conversation. He simply said that he had run and trained himself into a divorce to win this race and that we were just not committed enough to the cause. Who it was and what he won is not the point, it is about what you are prepared to sacrifice on the road to achievement.

Some are able to achieve enormous amounts whilst still maintaining a normal family life, or exercise routine. I am in awe of those who seem to have got it right, by being superb at what they do and exceptional at what they have achieved all the while they have strong relationships and have raised great children. There are others who seem prepared to sacrifice their family and relationships with their children for the sake of their careers. This is where it gets difficult. How much of a personal sacrifice is worth it, and for whom? I keep returning to the Lancet story. A new Lancet is published every month, in fact a new medical research article is published every 26 seconds. (Garba 2010) So yes, a Lancet paper might be forever but what is worth sacrificing to get one of thousands of papers to be published in the Lancet?

For each of us we will need to decide on the potential reward and its required sacrifice. We might cut out food to lose weight, others might go on starvation diets to protest injustice. How do we judge what is worth sacrificing, and how do we sift through what we see around us in the media, at home and in the work place to find our own motivation?

A friend working in the finance industry in New York, which has horrendous working hours, made the decision not to stay exceptionally late (after 8 p.m.) but to go home to his wife and children. There were others who would stay later to do the extra work and get credit with the added possibility of a promotion in the next cycle, but he had decided what his curfew was, and what was not worth sacrificing. He was content with his decision and the implications for his career by not staying as late as his colleagues.

The degree of sacrifice we might be willing to offer, will change during our lives. At certain points potentially more sacrifice for the same outcome will be required. At other times more sacrifice for less or potentially more reward will be needed. But at each point we can't be sure if the sacrifice will be worth it in the end.

I want to encourage those that feel strongly that they cannot sacrifice everything at the altar of success, wealth, promotion and recognition to reflect on the decision you are making and to be certain of your underlying motivations. You can be assured, you will be criticized for not doing enough, for not putting in enough effort to get the grant or win the award, for not staying at work way past your child's bed time. Provided your motivation for not making the sacrifice is what you ultimately want out of life, then watching your colleagues rise above you in academic promotion, with more publications and accolades is not as painful.

Unfortunately, as an academic one always has an uneasy feeling when you are not willing to sacrifice to the same extent as your colleagues. However, when I leave the office or clinic and go home, the things that I have chosen not to sacrifice counterbalances any lack of promotion or Lancet publication that may or may not have passed me by. It is important to be true to yourself, your family and your values, as these will be there with you when you receive the Nobel prize and even if you don't.

# 7. Warning Lights

Warning lights are interesting things and I have devoted a whole chapter to them. They are frequently dismissed as unnecessary or plainly ignored in the real world and similarly in our personal lives as well.

There is an old joke about a commander of a big ship who approaches what he thinks is a smaller ship. The commander hails the smaller ship instructing them to change their course, the response comes back: "No, you change course". Depending on who is telling the joke the narrative can go on for a while until the commander then tries to pull rank and bully the other ship. The commander informs the captain of the smaller boat that he is the commander of the USS Eisenhower, a nuclear-powered aircraft carrier and that he has right of way. The other captain must, without question and out of respect for his big ship change his course. This directive is met with a simple response of: "No, I am Petty Officer Littleworth in charge of the lighthouse and I suggest you change course."

This simple joke raises obvious issues surrounding the captain and his arrogance, for the purposes of this book, my emphasis is on the importance of lighthouses, which are very important, 'do or die' type warning lights. In our lives lighthouses function as important final warnings. You can't see a light house unless you are relatively close to one, and if it is far off in the distance, then they don't fulfil a great purpose. If we see them, we should clearly be paying attention to them, and not trying to ignore them. It would be better for all concerned if we paid attention to the early warning lights and any lighthouses in our vicinity and do not run aground on the rocks!

The second arena that warning lights are often a topic of review is in the airplane "crash investigator" type programs. The narrative frequently follows the same path where the pilot or crew noted the warning light, they ignored it at first, and then subsequently continued to ignore it, and switched it off when the beeping got too bad, until ultimately disaster struck and the airplane crashed.

A warning light comes on when something is not quite right and before a looming disaster. The idea is that if we see the light and do something about it, we will avoid something worse. The oil light in your car is a great example: It comes on and informs you that the level of oil in your engine is dangerously low, and you should do something soon to sort it out. If you don't add oil or stop driving your car you risk wrecking the engine. 'See the light and do something about it' seems like a simple analogy, but it raises several important issues for our lives in the real world: Firstly, you have to have them installed (thankfully our cars come with them); secondly, they must be in working order (unfortunately it is not always clear if they are working), and finally, you have to notice them and react appropriately.

Our cars come with a book which you will find in the cubby hole that actually tells us what each light is for and when it comes on what you should do. I confess that I have once or twice had to look in the book when a "new" light came on to work out what it was trying to tell me and what I should do, even though I have had the car for several years!

The warning lights in our own lives don't come pre-installed and there is no real manual to tell us what to do when they start flashing. In my life I did not see the warning lights and in reflecting, I am certain that I was not just ignoring them, I really did not see them. Having never seen them before, how was I to know that they were telling me something was amiss? Looking back now, it is much easier to see the course, to be shocked at how long the lights had been on and to reflect on why I had missed them. I have thought a lot about how I plan to not miss, nor ignore these warning lights going forward.

Warning lights in our personal and work lives remain complex things. We are trained to cope and coached to work hard. We are not trained to look for signs to indicate if we should take the day off, skip a meeting and go home early. If we do have warning lights in our lives, I would suggest that those regarding stress, anxiety or burn out do not trigger during the early stages. If they were early warning signs, they would be like an overly sensitive smoke detector, going off all the time for some of us. Instead we deny their existence, suppress their presence and place them on mute. We push these warning signs far away in the hope that they won't alarm us.

We don't really believe we have need of them because 'no one else seems to have them' and we regard them as a sign of weakness. Therefore, we consider them as a fail-safe to light up moments before impact. Somewhere deep down we don't really want to go over the edge. Again I would assume that this is not because of the injury it might cause, but because of the embarrassment and stigma associated with being seen as someone who can't cope. Even as crash warning lights, we probably would ignore them anyway, as we don't believe we, of all people, would be the ones likely to fail. We will cope, period.

I think that in our lives and work, these warning lights need to be visible and graded early warning systems that allow for notification when something can be done. They should also beep loudly when major problems appear on the horizon. I would like to suggest that these warning lights come in both internal and external forms. External warning signs are important and probably more reliable as they are less likely to being ignored.

However, they too need to be set in place and not easily dismissed. It is too easy to cancel or reschedule a meeting, or even forget to attend a mentoring session when we are far too busy.

Self-awareness is not something scientifically minded, analytical, performance orientated people spend a lot of time focused on. It distracts us from the tasks at hand and the goals ahead. I think we would do well to teach our students and younger colleagues to develop a greater sense of self awareness, to pause and to reflect and in so doing be more in tune with our feelings. The problem is that we have always been taught to 'suck it up'. We did it, so they should do it too. The high rate of suicide, drug abuse and divorce in the medical profession is testament to how well our copying system works. The playing field has also changed, as things occur at much faster rates, with higher demands for time and attention. No longer do we wait for the results to be faxed or a letter to arrive by post. We are all online all day, every day.

The basic questions my mentor and counsellor always asks me are: How are you eating and sleeping and are you getting any exercise? For me these have become simple warning lights that I can be mindful of. I am not sure these would work for everyone, but they are a useful starting point: sleep and food are probably universal while exercise could be swopped out for music, art, reading or spending time with friends to name a few alternatives. Finding a simple set of internal personal warning lights that you can be aware of is a good starting point. When more than one is flashing, one needs to review the reason for them being on. The next step is to identify when your life is going to change sufficiently in the next few days so that the balance can be restored and the lights will go off. Ignoring them is the first step down a path you do not wish to travel.

So how did I miss my warning lights? In hindsight some of my warning lights were anger, anxiety, social withdrawal and intolerance for simple demands made of me. I became angry far more easily than I normally would. My colleagues or staff would not have noticed as I am not the most volatile of people, but my children were getting short and dismissive responses from me. I also found my commute home (riddled with taxis) provoked more anger in me. I would avoid listening to the news on the radio or reading the newspaper.

Driving to work simply made me even more anxious, increasing the intensity of that gnawing feeling I had every day when I woke up. I had just ascribed it to dyspepsia, despite taking omeprazole! I did not wish to talk to people, just in case they asked me to do something. I avoided emails and hated phone calls as they inevitably involved somebody asking me to do something, or even worse, it could be a crisis or rejection from a journal or grant application. I put my behaviour down to being stressed at work with a heavy burden, too many things to do and a slightly chaotic world around me. I did not know that my change in behaviour were glaring warning lights.

For others these warning lights might be altered sleep patterns, a change in appetite or eating patterns, changes to your usual interactions with colleagues, a lack of motivation or drive. Finding comfort in unhealthy options like binge eating, alcohol and illicit drugs are the more obvious warning lights. They will look different for each unique person, but the starting point which we can all look out for is a change in our normal behaviours or attitudes.

It was not until I sat in front of a trained therapist (who I had gone to see for a completely different reason) that the penny finally dropped and I realised what was going on. Yes, I was aware that things were a little stressful and that I had this ache in my stomach on some days. However, I only realised where I had ended up when listening to someone else point out to me that what I was experiencing might not be entirely normal. What I thought were some days was actually every day for months! I don't wish to go into detail about the whole process and other events occurring around this time, but what I heard was enough to concede and, somewhat reluctantly, I began to take medication.

I was loathe to admit that I could not cope, but the truth of the matter is that I wasn't coping. The way I felt about it made no difference. I was not ready to tell the world I was taking medication for anxiety. I also dreaded the day I would have to fill out an insurance form and tick the box which asks if you suffer from or have been treated for any mental illness. My ego was in tatters.

Unfortunately, at this initial recognition point when I started taking the medication, I was not able to make changes to the situations I found myself in. There were several highly stressful circumstances that were totally out of my control. This however changed when one Friday morning, sitting at my desk looking up at the mountain, I finally phoned a trusted colleague and described how I was having severe central chest pain. A band around my chest was tightening and I felt like I could not breathe. I was pretty certain that I was not having a heart attack, and that I was just making it all up, but I could not go on. Once I was medically cleared and booked off work, we began the process of identifying what I could change, what I could not change, and what I was going to do about it. I no longer wanted to simply cope, I had to makes realistic changes to my work and lifestyle leading towards sustainability.

One of the critical interventions was focussing on my down time. Whilst making changes at work, I also needed to make changes outside of work to ensure that the intensity of my work was balanced with the intensity of my down time. I cannot begin to tell you how strange it felt, when after several months, I cautiously asked my wife what normal felt like, as I thought I might be feeling normal again.

# 8. Downtime

One of the things I have learnt through this process is the importance of down time. Thankfully I am quite good at switching in and out of work mode. Clearly not good enough (as I still hit the rocks) but efficient enough to cope far too long before crashing anyway.

Downtime in sporting terms is often referred to as periodization, or active recovery. You can't train hard every day and every week. You have to have hard days and rest days, hard weeks and gentle weeks. Some months are more intense and others less intense. In medicine particularly, our patients, workloads and research demands don't follow this pattern. There are always patients in every clinic. Each day a whole lot of new patients pitch up in the emergency room; as you discharge one ICU patient the next one arrives. On top of a clinical load there are academic, student and research demands. These might have some sort of periodization, but that is the only difference. If one is not preparing for lectures, you may be presenting them or marking assignments. If not applying for grants, you may be doing the work or writing up the results whilst applying for the next grant. The scenery might change but the work continues.

Athletes have learnt that resting between events that stress the body improves performance. Rest is often as important as a training day. When our work and life demands continue day in and day out, we are heading for disaster if we don't develop a resilience, through coping mechanisms and more importantly structured down time. Resilience and coping mechanisms are best coached by professionals, and so I am not going to delve into this area as I am not an expert. It is crucial to see an expert and receive training in this if we are to start thriving again.

A simple but apt example of the importance of taking down time was when I was a medicine registrar in 2003. I worked at the old GF Jooste Hospital in Manenberg; a low income, high crime area with frequent gang related violence. We were short of medical registrars and there was little prospect of getting any relief any time soon. In those days we only had a consultant ward round in the hospital twice a week and the rest of the time we were on our own. Because of safety concerns, we did not travel in or out of the hospital at night.

We had a separate male and female medical ward and a daily bed occupancy of around 120%: Each day we would admit at least 20 men and 20 women, and need to discharge the same number. There were only two registrars for most of the month and so we simply split the two wards. I took the male ward and my colleague took the female ward. We would take casualty referrals for patients needing admission to the hospital all day and then after 4pm the casualty staff would admit sick patients directly to the ward as we were not in the hospital after dark. The following morning, we would pick up a pile of 10-15 folders of the patients who had been admitted overnight, see them all and then start fielding the new referrals for the day. The same occurred each day of the week.

The two of us survived that month! We would usually meet to eat our lunch together or at least have coffee. We covered for each other when on call overnight and at around 4:30 p.m. each day we went home. Partly due to personal safety, but primarily as that was all we could manage. We needed the down time after work to be able to cope with what would happen on the next day. Neither of us will ever forget that experience, but we survived. Admittedly our service was not necessarily world class, we could probably have done more, but we chose to do our best whilst preserving ourselves. We chose not to sacrifice ourselves in the process.

When working clinically, I have always tried to follow a principle I learnt from a gynaecology registrar when I was an intern. I refer to it as the principle of: There is no point in both of us being awake. As a junior doctor on call for gynaecology emergencies, the usual process late at night was for the registrar on call to be bleeped (before cell phones!), by the casualty officer. They would then phone the intern who would go and see the patient and report back to the registrar who would later come to review what you had done. The registrar would make a final decision to sort the problem out and often it meant moving to theatre.

However, this particular gynaecology registrar would not wake me when called if she knew that ultimately she was going to have to sort the problem out by taking the patient to theatre. Since she was awake she would just get it done herself. Why have both of us awake? Of course it is not always possible to apply this principle and sometimes it takes two to get the job done, but just because there are two of us who could do it, does not mean we both have to be woken up. Applying this principle in day time hours similarly frees one of us up to get something else done or even just to have a short break.

The following year I worked in the UK as a Senior House officer and I worked my longest ever shifts in a large central London renal unit. We would often get our work done before 4 p.m. on any given day. However, from the time we finished our work until 4 p.m. we had to just sit around. I could not fathom the concept of waiting until 4 p.m. doing nothing except talking rubbish (in those days before Twitter and Facebook) and then going home. This was how we had to work and leaving early was not an option. What if we left one person in charge so that the rest of the team could get an early start home? What if we could provide down time for each other when the opportunity arose?

I am aware we have working hours and tasks that must be performed but maybe we could lighten each other's loads whenever possible by holding the fort to allow the other some down time. For example: "I will finish the clinic, you can get coffee" or "I will cover the clinic this afternoon as it is quiet. Go home and watch the kids play cricket". These down times during our working weeks, allow us to catch our breath, to restore our souls and to see the outside world in the midst of the relentless chaos that our jobs and schedules demand. Ultimately things probably will continue as normal at work even if we are not there, but if we end up #@%^&'d, whatever we are meant to do will not happen anyway.

Down time outside of work also requires attention. Not getting enough time to play with the kids, go to the gym, read books or go to the movies, for example, is a problem. Yes we do have busy weeks on call when these leisure activities are not possible, but let's return to the athlete analogy. You have to have rest days, your body needs time to recover between hard effort, and your mind needs down time and you need to breathe.

As a junior registrar, I used to come home and flick through channels on TV, without satellite there were only four channels! Certainly not the most ideal activity but it got my mind off work and helped me to focus on something else. Down time may look different for others and one may need professional input to figure out what works best for you.

At the height of my recent high stress period I played candy crush (a super addictive cell phone game that was great at taking my mind off work). It unfortunately kept my mind active, I was not engaging with my family and I used it as a place to hide. It was certainly not a good coping mechanism. I didn't recognize that it was problematic until it was pointed out to me and a conscious decision was required to delete it from my devices. Amusingly it precipitated a very quizzical inquiry from my sons as to why dad was no longer playing candy crush!

I am in no way qualified to suggest what sort of down time would work for each person, however I do think that the activities should be fulfilling, non-work related and, in some way, restoring. I even took up oil painting, which was great as I could only do a little painting and then was forced to wait until the paint dried to carry on again. The canvass remained on the table and I would spend 10 or 15 minutes painting before heading off to my next activity.

For each of us we need to find that recharging activity that gives us enough boost, energy and restoration to balance the draining aspects of a normal day. Activities that just numb the pain and stress are not constructive, they do not help us gain resilience in the face of a 'very hot kitchen' of challenging circumstances. Taking the analogy further; if the temperature in the kitchen is going to remain high for a while, then we need to work out how to cope, and cope well, not just survive.

# 9. Working within Margins

The concept of living within margins was the topic of conversation on a Saturday morning mountain bike ride with my friend. There is actually a book on this topic entitled: Margin: restoring emotional, physical, financial and time reserves to overloaded lives. The author Richard Swenson provides the following definition of a margin: *"Margin is the space between our load and our limits. It is the amount allowed beyond that which is needed. It is something held in reserve for contingencies or unanticipated situations. Margin is the gap between rest and exhaustion, the space between breathing freely and suffocating". (Swenson 2004)*

The idea is that if we have margins, or space between our current effort and our limits, we are less likely to burn out. Two illustrations come to mind: You can't burn a candle at both ends, and, you can't exceed the stretch of the elastic without breaking it.

It will be hard to set our margins if we don't know our limits. This too requires reflection and attention to our own needs so that we can work out where our limits lie.

It also requires a degree of honesty in admitting that we are not Superman or Wonder Woman, and that we might be incapable of constant peak performance. It will require humility to recognize that we are not indestructible.

It is worth asking the following questions: What if I do not accept every request coming my way? What if I want to say no because I can't handle any more work? Will others think I am unhelpful or not a team player, or worse still, that I lack commitment or determination? Most of the time our saying 'no' is entangled in far too much personal baggage about our self-worth.

The reality remains that if we are burnt out and stressed beyond our ability to cope, we are not going to be capable of doing anything valuable or helpful. We are living in a consumer society where most products are disposable. If they break, you simply buy a replacement. Most are irreparable, so they are disposed of when they fail. I suspect that this approach has also crept into the work force to some extent. Would it not be better for us all if we understood our limits, if we knew when the answer needed to be 'no', and that our reasons would not questioned?

I do not wish to provide a trite "Ten ways to say no without feeling guilty and still appearing great". However, I want to suggest that we need to be real with ourselves first and recognize our own limits. Then only can we say 'no' with a degree of conviction, knowing that it is not a sign of weakness, but actually a sign of strength and self-awareness. The harder challenge then, would be for all of us to accept a 'no' from someone else without thinking less of them. How refreshing it would be if our 'no' was accepted and respected instead of it triggering a manipulative rebuttal pointing out how much we would lose if we "refused" to help or how our selfishness could hamper our career progression.

Of course those that frequently say 'no' may well be unhelpful sluggards. It is exceptionally frustrating when one is working very hard and an assistant who clearly is not busy simply refuses to help. Too often we have heard people say: "I am about to go home, wait for the next shift" or, "I am on my break" or, "It is not my job to do that." Not for a moment am I suggesting unhelpfulness, but I am realising and appreciating that everyone needs a short break from time to time, and perhaps it will be better to ask for their help after that break.

We need to be clear about our underlying motivation for accepting or rejecting the requests directed our way. In addition, we need to understand our margins and where we are in relation to them at any given point in time. We need to incorporate enough 'slack' in our functioning capacity so that when another request comes, we have the capacity to offer the help required. As mentioned earlier, in my lowest moments I dreaded any phone call or email, as I just did not have the capacity to deal with anything more. Not that the calls or emails were all requests for my help, but the mere possibility was enough to heighten my anxiety levels.

I recognize that in an overloaded health care system, where patient lives are at stake, taking frequent breaks to re-centre ourselves is not necessarily the solution. We need more staff, with better pay and longer vacations. Unfortunately this is a pipe dream in most situations. So, the question remains for all of us working in such a system: How can I work within my capacity margins?

Team leaders need to ask: How can we work as a team within the necessary margins to deliver the service, but not destroy the workers at the same time? Self-reflection and space to consider the situation is required. Whilst fighting a fire, the fireman does not think about fire prevention, but it nonetheless needs to be addressed because relentlessly fighting a fire every day is simply not sustainable.

sikelela

64

## 10.    The People in your Corner

In boxing matches the people in your corner, who motivate you, keep you hydrated and stop you from bleeding too much, are critical if you are to survive all 12 rounds. In this book I am not advocating mere survival as the goal, however, having people in your corner and staying alive (to receive a Nobel prize) remain a good idea.

Your corner will look different to mine, but I hope that through my own personal perspective as a married man with two small children, that I can draw out some examples and provide some ideas.

I first met my wife at a party on a Friday afternoon at Clifton beach, a few weeks before my final medical specialist exams called the FCP. For those who know me, you will immediately recognise the potential problems with this scenario: It had been a long working week, there was a lot of traffic *en route* to Clifton, I was in pre-exam mode and add to that my somewhat introverted nature. Needless to say, I did not make a very good impression on the young lady!

Thankfully she had shared a flat with several other doctors who had gone through the horrors of preparing for the monster FCP exam. By the time we finally got married, she fully understood what exams, on call and work entailed. She does not work in the medical arena but understands enough to know the lay of the land. She is far enough removed to question my 'must' and 'have to' statements. Having a solid supporter who can support me when the waves are high, but also call me out of the water when the sharks are circling is priceless.

I don't think I appreciated quite how important the people in my corner are to me. I was never left completely alone without support and was able to take time out to meet with people who had similar values to my own. One could argue that they merely reinforced my own prejudices, but they provided some sense of normality as they negotiated their own struggles, they walked beside me in the chaos I was experiencing. With these people I was able to process my disappointments and failures and celebrate my success, away from the spotlight. It was important to be known for who I was and not what I did. We tend to get so caught up in our own worlds and what we consider to be normal that we forget the reality outside of our own box.

The challenge is to find the people in your box with whom you can be honest. The shame associated with not coping in academia prevents many from voicing their struggles. People tend to stay quietly in the corners, keeping their heads down in order to avoid being passed over and identified as incapable. I have yet to find many who I can talk to and encourage on this journey, which in part, fuelled my inspiration for this book.

The place where I found guidance was not in a therapy group, or with a counsellor, but on a mountain bike, riding with a friend on a Saturday morning. We are from completely different work environments, but oddly share similar frustrations and challenges. Whilst not appealing to many, we regularly rode up a route known as heartbreak hill on the face of Table Mountain. This particular hill is steep enough to get admiring or dumbfounded expressions from fellow riders when they realise where we are headed. The challenge was to make it to the top and past the tree without putting a foot down. It was not so much the activity but about getting away from our normal day to day stress. We would share our frustrations and fears whilst riding on a beautiful mountain. We came down from the mountain better people, having dispelled the angst of the week and burnt some calories, and (if we were on form) having conquered the hill by passing the tree without stopping.

Before writing this book, I chose to share my story with our church at the annual thanksgiving service. It seemed appropriate to share this story, not that God had miraculously saved me from the abyss or that I was cured, but that there was grace through the journey. Apart from the fact that many medical people attend our church, an unanticipated consequence was the freedom it brought. Sharing my journey with people, many of whom I don't know very well, took much of the shame and guilt off my shoulders. I was open to being seen as broken, open to being asked how I was doing and open to hear of others' struggles as in voicing mine I had given them hope and inspiration. The next step was writing this book!

Not everyone needs to know my story, but I suspect there are many who have a story and have not been able to share it, for fear of shame and ridicule. Vulnerability in sharing who we are is not a weakness, but it requires enough people in your corner that know you well enough to clean the blood and dirt off your face and help you back on your feet.

70

# 11.    Concluding Thoughts

Having been through the fire and out the other side has given me the opportunity to reflect on what I do, why I do it and how I intend to move forward. I have not had a mid-life crisis and bought a fancy car or taken up shark cage diving. I have, however had to admit, that despite my apparent success, achievements and accolades, I remain human with cracks. I do not blame the system or wish this had never happened, but I have acknowledged that I am not as super human as I originally thought.

A friend once said that we are all so grateful when we expect the worst and it doesn't happen, when we dodge a bullet or say "that was too close". But what if the worst thing actually did happen (like it did for her family)? How then do we respond? They are still standing, but horribly battered. That is their reality. For some of us we have dodged a bullet, or sustained only flesh wounds; either way, we need to live with our brokenness as best we can.

I hope that my story and reflections on it will help lead those in crisis to seek professional help. It should not be a patch up job, but a restoration project where you plan for the future. I don't think I am as tough as I used to be. I have tested my boundaries and now know very well where they are and how much margin I have to spare before I break. I have come to terms with that, and plan for long term sustainability. That means I am prepared to miss the potential exceptional peaks of academic brilliance, but I intend on remaining alive to celebrate my accomplishments!

For those not in crisis, I hope these reflections might highlight potential dangers up ahead and provide you with food for thought. Take the time now to put your warning lights in strategic and visible places. Set your margins and plan for sustainability and performance, balancing the sacrifices and achievements for yourself.

For those who remain unconvinced that failure is an option, those with an unlimited ability to achieve and those who consider sacrifices as non-negotiable: I hope you will realize that we are not all built like that and others' priorities may be different, with margins set below your required threshold. These margins are set not because we are incapable, but because we are exceptionally capable. We recognize our frailty and need to set boundaries so that we will be here for the long haul, and not just for short term glory.

Finally, I would like to propose that we are of far more value to our families, friends, colleagues, patients and society as a whole when we are alive and performing within margins, rather than dead, with or without a Nobel prize.

# 12. Questioning Faith

Initially I did not plan to include a chapter on faith and its role in my journey, however several people asked me about it when they were assisting with the original drafts of this book. So, with repeated prompting I have included a discussion of faith in this chapter.

I had been prompted to share my story at church partly as a way of bringing it into the light, to break some of the associated guilt and shame. Sharing my story was also a testimony of grace through trials. I was certainly not healed or cured, but I was on a journey and through the trials I saw grace around me.

Following this, a mother whose young daughter had recently died also chose to share her story of grace through trials at church. How we often thank God when we have a near miss saying things such as: "I nearly crashed my car, but God was there with me" or "I had cancer, but God was there and I'm now in remission". For this mother, her daughter died, and God was there with her. God is there with you, even in that situation when the worst that you could imagine happens.

There are no trite answers as to why God allowed it to happen. Through this process of having a grounded faith, I have had to acknowledge that I cannot cope on my own, that I am in need of God's sustaining presence. Even when I had panic attacks at 3 a.m. when I felt like I was all alone, God was there with me. Yes, I questioned things and wished it would be over, and asked 'why me?'. I had to get over my pride to realise that I was not coping. Even as an academic clinician, with a PhD, running a research unit and having over 50 publications including a Lancet paper (ok, Lancet Respiratory), I was not coping. I was exercising my talents, using my gifts in what I considered to be my calling and yet I was suffering from an anxiety disorder. Had I got it wrong? Had I missed something along the way? Was I walking along the wrong career path? I think these are natural questions one asks when things do not pan out as you expect them to.

I did not really question my faith in this process, but I am sure others have or will do so. For me the process emphasised my reliance on God and His assurance that I was not alone: grace through trials. The trial did not go away, the dark was still dark, and the sound of lions roaring around me was still intense. The story of Shadrack, Meshack and Abednego meant a lot to me as I pondered how to live well in the fire. If the fire was not going to consume me, but was still intensely around me, how could I live without getting burnt? I know God has been with me through this process and has not let go of me. It was not easy to get up each day and look forward to very little, but there was a call to go on.

### ###

During this time several songs have been on repeat, and loudly too. I am sure there are many others worth listening to, but here are some that I listened to in the hardest times:

*In over my head* – by Jenn Johnson:
"I'm going under, I'm in over my head
Whether I sink, whether I swim
Oh it makes no difference when I'm beautifully in over my head"

*You're gonna be ok* – by Brian and Jenn Johnson:
"Just take, one step, closer
Put one foot in front of the other
You'll, get through this
Just follow the light in the darkness
You're gonna be ok"

*Alibi* - by Thirty Seconds to Mars
"No warning sign, no alibi
We're fading faster than the speed of light.
Took our chance, crashed and burned.
No, we'll never ever learn.
I fell apart, but got back up again,
And then I fell apart, but got back up again, yeah."

### 

I was holding on for dear life and my faith held onto me. It did not solve the problem or make it go away, it simply held me. The promises I know to be true; that I would not be forsaken, that I am made in His image, that I am a child of God, these promises held me. On some nights and early mornings all I was capable of doing was reciting the Lord's Prayer, over and over again. I held onto truth in the midst of anguish. I was not cured and the burden had not lifted, but I had grace to hold on.

This may not be your experience of faith, or what you expect, but it was part of my faith story. It has brought me to where I am currently, which is partly why you are reading this!

I would not wish this experience on anyone. I would not wish to go through it again and to some extent I wish I could have avoided it, but I am thankful for the lessons I have learnt, how I have grown and how this experience has moulded me. I would prefer not to be known as the flawed academic consultant who can't cut it in academia and suffers from a stress induced anxiety disorder. However, I am prepared to be vulnerable on this issue so that my staff, my students, my colleagues and my friends have someone who can empathise, support and encourage them if similar situations arise in their lives.

There is redemption in this story, that through my experience I might be able to support others. I certainly do not want to go on a book or speaking tour telling this story over and over, but if it is of help, then that is what I will do. My encouragement to all of us is to own our stories, our fights and our struggles. We must do this not so that we can console one another or feel sorry for each other, but so that we can make an impact in a highly pressured and demanding system. We can, with honesty and truth, show that we can cope, that we can achieve, and that through grace, we can endure these trials.

Ultimately faith is part of who I am and it has provided a great deal of perspective in this journey. There really is more to life than achievement, it is not about what I do, but about who I am. My value and self-worth are not dependent on my success at work or in publications, but in who I am. This is not an excuse to not work hard but it is an attitude that says: there is more to life than this and I will not be defined by my failure or my success.

Having likeminded people of faith around me has certainly helped as I grapple with my anxiety and how I negotiate the demands of academia and medicine.

Using the words of Jeremy Camp, "I will walk by faith when I cannot see."

# Acknowledgements

Heather, Timothy and Oliver for walking through the valley with me. Duncan, Charlie, Pete and Nikki for seeing what I could not and holding me accountable. Craig for hours of Sabbath rest on mountain bike trails. Elizabeth and Rose for tea and prayers. To my immediate and extended family for navigating through my absence. Cheryl for believing. Bronwyn for sweeping up the glass of dropped balls. Tom and Alphonso for regular life reflections over 'eggs benedict'. My team for holding the fort when I could not. My colleagues for their examples and inspiration.

## About the Illustrator

Zach Stewart is a bold and courageous young person completing his schooling this year. He engages deeply with the world as evident by his drawings and was willing to share his artistic perspective on the themes of the book.

# References

Brown, B. (2012). <u>Daring Greatly: how the courage to be vulnerable transforms the way we live, love, parent, and lead</u>. USA, Gotham Hardcover books

Garba, S., A. Ahmed, A. Mai, et. al (2010). "Proliferations of scientific medical journals: a burden or a blessing." <u>Oman Med J</u> **25**(4): 311-314.

Oreskovich, M. R., K. L. Kaups, et. al (2012). "Prevalence of alcohol use disorders among American surgeons." <u>Arch Surg</u> **147**(2): 168-174.

Ratatatouille. (2007). Retrieved 10 June 2018, 2018, from <u>https://en.wikiquote.org/wiki/Ratatouille</u>.

Roosevelt, T. (1910). Retrieved 3 June 2018, 2018, from <u>http://www.theodore-roosevelt.com/trsorbonnespeech.html</u>

Swenson, R. (2004). <u>Margin: Restoring Emotional, Physical, Financial, and Time Reserves to Overloaded Lives</u>. Canada, Navpress.

Printed in Great Britain
by Amazon

33694539R00050